This book belongs to

....

Age ....

Published in Great Britain in 1997 by
World International Ltd., Deanway Technology Centre,
Wilmslow Road, Handforth, Cheshire SK9 3FB.
Printed in Great Britain
ISBN 0 7498 3387 4

Written by John Broadhead and Joyce McAleer
Illustrated by Alan Willow

Contents

Bing, Bong!

I. It was New Year's Eve and Matthew was staying at Castle McBong. He had invited Sooty, Sweep, Soo and Scampi to a party.

"Oh, dear, this doesn't look a very lively place. There's not even a light on," said Soo, looking at the gloomy castle.

2. "Good evening, sir. We've come for the party!" said Sooty. The big man at the door looked very puzzled but he welcomed them in.

3. There wasn't a lot of food – and it didn't seem much like a party. "I wonder where Matthew is?" whispered Sooty.

6

4. Time for bed ... and Sooty, Sweep, Soo and Scampi climbed the stairs. "It's very cold and lonely here," said Scampi with a shiver.

5. But they were not alone. "Aargh!" yelled Soo at the top of her voice. "Run for it boys!" Not that they needed telling!

6. Sweep was scared. He jumped up and hung onto a candle holder. But it opened a secret doorway, and they all swung into the wall.

7. "We're in trouble," squeaked Sweep. "I can feel it in my bones!" There was nowhere to go but follow the mysterious path ahead.

8. Sooty led the way, followed by Sweep and Soo. But none of them saw Scampi step on a trapdoor and disappear into the ground.

9. "Where has Scampi gone? He's *so* naughty!" said Soo, as they came to a river. They climbed into an old boat tied up there.

10. Sooty rowed the boat out into the loch. A huge monster popped up. She was friendly and said that she was on holiday from Loch Ness!

11. The boat was turned upside down, and Sooty, Sweep and Soo fell into the freezing water. "Brrr!" they all yelled.

12. Scampi to the rescue! The trapdoor had dropped him into the castle garden. Now he was here to save them ...

13. Was this *another* ghost? "Oh, it's just Mr McBong," sighed Soo. "No, I'm not McBong," he cried. "My name's *McBing*!"

14. "We came to the *wrong* castle!" giggled Soo. Mr McBing took them round to Castle McBong on the other side of the loch.

15. Sooty and his pals were in time to enjoy the party. Sooty and Sweep were not very good at dancing – but they soon learned!

Rogues' Gallery

Sooty has got a camera for Christmas and he's started a photo album. It's a great way to keep your photographs from getting lost. Just like Sooty, you can write little notes by the side of each picture...

Sooty Here I am! Everyone's favourite bear! Mums and dads love me too – just ask them! I may not say a lot, but I'm definitely the leader of the gang. Can you guess my favourite song? It's *Teddy Bears' Picnic*, of course!

Sweep Bones, bones and *more* bones... that's what my friend Sweep has on the brain. The rest of the time he's either thinking of sausages or planning his next naughty trick. His favourite food is *bones on toast!*

Soo Soo loves to join in the fun with the rest of the gang. But when she raises her voice we all have to sit up and *listen*. Her favourite TV programme? Anything in *black and white*!

Scampi Cheeky Scampi wears a school blazer and cap... but usually looks as if he's slept in them. His favourite subject is *Matthew-matics!*

Sooty's Rib Ticklers

"What's the difference between a panda and a postbox?"
"I don't know."
"Well, I'd better not let you post my letters!"

What gets wetter and wetter the more it dries?
– A towel!

How do we know bears like Penguins?
– I've seen the empty wrappers in Sooty's bedroom!

What does Sweep use to smarten himself up?
– A sweeping brush!

"Knock, knock ..."
"Who's there?"
"Soo."
"Soo who?"
"Sooner you open up, sooner you'll know!"

Mummy, Mummy... I think I'm turning into Sweep!
– I thought you looked a little wuff this morning!

Why are bungalows so-called?
– Because the builders just bung a low roof on!

Why does Sooty feel the cold in winter?
– Because he has bear legs!

Sooty's Box of Tricks

Sooty is famous for his magic. He's been doing tricks for a long time but his friends still can't work out how he does them. Here are some of his favourites for *you* to try, and you won't even need a wand! If you're interested in magic, look in your library for books of tricks. Now, izzy wizzy, let's get busy!

Pick a Card

Fan out a pack of playing-cards and ask a friend to remove one, remember it and put it back *anywhere* in the pack. You then straighten up the pack, flick through it and pick out the card your friend chose.

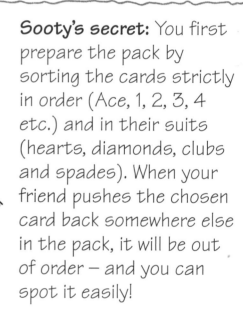

Sooty's secret: You first prepare the pack by sorting the cards strictly in order (Ace, 1, 2, 3, 4 etc.) and in their suits (hearts, diamonds, clubs and spades). When your friend pushes the chosen card back somewhere else in the pack, it will be out of order – and you can spot it easily!

Defying Gravity

You can amaze people by telling them you can cover a beaker of water with a drinks-mat and hold it upside-down without spilling it.

Sooty's secret: Just fill a plastic drinking glass to the brim with water. Then place a drinks-mat on top and hold it in place with a finger whilst you turn the drinking glass upside-down. When you remove your finger the mat should remain in place and the water will stay in the beaker. It's like real magic, but **always** do it over a sink or bowl to avoid a mess!

Which Box?

Place three matchboxes on the table. Shake two to show a friend they're empty; then rattle the third, saying it has a button inside. Swizzle the boxes around and then ask your friend to point to the one with the button. You can make sure they always get it wrong ... but how?

Sooty's secret: The three matchboxes are really **all** empty. You have another matchbox, with a button in, hidden in the cuff of your right hand. Whenever you shake an empty box with that hand, it appears to rattle; when you shake a box with your left hand, it sounds empty!

Balloon that won't pop

Tell your pals you can stick a pin in an inflated balloon without popping it. They won't believe you – until you astonish them by doing it!

Sooty's secret: Have a small square of sticky tape stuck to the balloon. You can then stick the pin through it and, with luck, the balloon won't burst. **Always** ask a grown-up before using a pin!

Mind Reading

Ask someone to select a number from 1 to 5 and tell them you *know* what they're going to say. When they give you the number, tell them to look under a chair-cushion and they'll find you've already written their number on a little piece of paper.

Sooty's secret: You simply place a **different** number under each cushion in the room. Whatever number your pal says, you direct them to the appropriate cushion. But don't do the trick more than once on the same occasion, or they'll guess how you do it!

THE PAIN IN SPAIN

1. Sooty, Sweep, Soo and Scampi had a *great* time when they went on holiday to Spain. But for poor Matthew it was a real pain!

2. On the plane Scampi went to the toilet. He was a long time, so Matthew went to get him.

3. "Out you come...or there'll be trouble," he joked, banging on the toilet door.

4. The door opened and a young lady came out. "How dare you!" she cried, and she hit him with the newspaper.

5. Everyone laughed as Matthew ran back to his seat!

6. At last they were in Spain. Matthew now had a black eye but he couldn't wait to enjoy the sun.

7. "I'll use plenty of sun cream," he said, splashing himself with white stuff. "I found this tube in the hotel bathroom. Now for a snooze!"

8. He found a sunny place in the shade of a trellis fence and went to sleep on his chair.

9. "Matthew, you're in big trouble!" cried Soo, waking him later. "Your tube of cream was *toothpaste*!"

10. Matthew felt his skin. "Ouch!" he yelled. "I'm burned!" "And what a pity you fell asleep behind that fence," giggled Soo. "Because you're now covered in sunburn diamonds!"

11. "Waaah!" screamed Matthew.

12. On the beach, poor Matthew looked so silly that everyone laughed at him.

13. He stepped backwards and fell over a big sandcastle.

14. The angry man who had just made it chased him – and gave him another black eye!

15. Lunchtime came and everyone was hungry.

16

16. Antonio, the waiter, winked at Soo. "Such a beautiful lady," he smiled.

17. He went away and came back with a huge plate of Spanish food. From it he pulled a jar of honey for Sooty, a tasty bone for Sweep, and flowers for Soo.

18. "What's in it for me?" asked Matthew. He was shocked when Antonio pulled out an octopus.

17

19. "There is something else..." said Antonio. Then little Scampi popped up from the plate of food.

20. In the afternoon Sooty and the gang went to the market.

21. "Where's Soo?" said Matthew. A big car drove up with Antonio and Soo inside. "Antonio is showing me round," smiled Soo. "See you all later!"

22. Later they all met in the disco. Matthew looked very odd with two black eyes and his skin covered with diamond patterns.

24. Another girl appeared. Matthew got up again to dance. But she pointed at Sweep. "No, no...with the little dog, I mean," she said.

23. He was pleased when a Spanish girl came and asked for a dance. "Not with *you*, grandfather... with the little bear, please!" said the girl.

25. Then Antonio came up and asked Soo to dance.

26. Matthew and Scampi were left alone, so they had to dance *together*!

27. For Sooty and the rest of the gang, the end of the holiday came all too quickly.

28. "I'll miss Spain," Matthew said sadly, standing by the side of the swimming pool.

29. Soo tried to tell him he was too near the edge but he didn't listen.

30. "Bye bye, everyone, bye bye," he said, and then he stepped right into the pool and landed in the water with a huge splash!

31. How Sooty, Sweep, Soo and Scampi laughed at their silly friend. He had black eyes, diamond patterns on his skin...and now he was soaking wet for the trip home.

Sweep's Sausage Factory

Sweep's got sausages on the brain! Help him have fun finding the words at the bottom of the page in this big word square puzzle, then draw sausage shapes round them. Look carefully – the words may read backwards or forwards, or even from bottom to top. The first two are done for you!
(*Answers on page 60.*)

S	W	E	E	P	L	N	P	S	E
C	A	N	U	Q	O	S	T	O	A
A	E	N	X	S	B	E	N	O	B
M	O	U	V	S	V	W	K	L	I
P	N	C	A	M	P	E	R	T	V
I	N	H	N	D	Q	P	A	B	H
V	W	S	C	N	S	O	O	T	Y
M	A	G	I	C	U	I	A	B	U
K	N	W	E	Z	N	S	I	Q	V
S	D	A	W	E	H	T	T	A	M

√ 1. WAND   2. SOO.   3. SCAMPI   4. MATTHEW   5. CAMPER
6. VAN   7. BONE   8. MAGIC   9. SWEEP   10. SOOTY

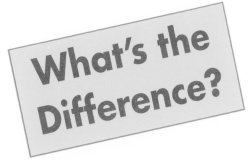
What's the Difference?

Look closely at these two pictures of Sooty and the gang washing the camper van. You'll find they're not quite the same. Can you spot the five differences between them? (*Answers on page 60.*)

Make Sooty's Theatre

In days gone by, miniature theatres were very popular toys. It's easy to make your own model of Sooty's Theatre with a strong shoe box, some spare card, sticky tape, glue and a few odds and ends. But always ask a grown-up to do the cutting for you ...

1. Cut holes in the ends of the shoe box.

2. Add a fancy front cut from card and glue it on with little tabs. Decorate and colour it.

3. Add some curtains made of bright crêpe paper left over from Christmas.

4. Trace the figures of Sooty, Sweep, Soo and Scampi below and stick them onto stiff card. Colour them and then tape or glue a length of stiff card or a lolly stick to the base of each one.

When you're ready for the show, simply push and pull Sooty & Co. on and off the stage from the side. For a more spectacular performance, darken the room and shine a powerful torch onto your theatre from across the room!

Sooty Airlines

"Why are *you* reading my letter, Soo?" asked Matthew, coming down the stairs in his pyjamas.

"Sweep opened it by mistake," said Soo. "Remember that airline you lent some money to? It's in danger of closing down – and now it's all *yours*!"

Matthew pulled a face. "But I don't want an *airline*!"

Sooty and Sweep looked hard at one another, then Sooty whispered in Matthew's ear.

"What!?" laughed Matthew. "*You* want to run it? Ha, you'll never get it off the ground!"

24

Next day Sooty's camper van arrived at Crashbang Airlines. But what a shock Sooty and the gang had. Their new airline was nothing but a shed and two old, patched-up planes.

But with a little work, Sooty Airlines was soon ready for business.

Sooty stood with Soo, the air-stewardess, and welcomed their first passengers. Engineer Scampi wiped his oily hands on his clothes and saluted smartly.

Sweep was the pilot for the day. But when the passengers saw him looping-the-loop in the plane, they ran off in fear.

Sooty was *so* disappointed. Then Sweep's daring flying tricks gave him a brilliant idea – Sooty's Aerobatics Display Team!

"Roll up, roll up! See Sooty and Sweep the Super Skyfliers!" cried Soo to the crowds of people who came to the airfield next day. Scampi was selling lots of tickets for the show.

The two old planes took off, and Sooty and Sweep flew around the sky and then zoomed low. The thick, black smoke from their engines made everyone cough.

Sweep grinned even more widely. He waved Sooty to follow him. They flew away towards town. Sweep pointed downwards. Sooty saw that they were directly over the Sooty & Co. shop. Matthew heard the roar of the engines and came out to look. Sweep squealed in delight, then pulled a little lever. A big bag of flour dropped from his plane. Down it went! Matthew saw it coming. He tried to run but didn't know which way to go. Splat! The bag burst on

his head and turned him instantly into a living snowman.

"Waaah!" he yelled. "You two should be banned!"

"I hope that naughty pair have enough petrol," sighed Soo, back at the airfield.

Scampi gulped and looked very guilty. He saw two cans of petrol standing nearby. He had forgotten to fill the planes!

Then Sooty and Sweep's engines spluttered. The planes stopped in the air and plunged down towards the park. With a loud crunching and hissing, they crashed into the pond – followed by Sooty and Sweep on parachutes. Splosh! Splosh!

And that, sadly, was the end of Sooty Airlines. Unless *you* have a couple of planes to lend them!

Sooty in Sherwood

I. Sooty and his friends were driving through Sherwood Forest. "I wish we were here in Robin Hood's days!" squeaked Sweep.

He waved Sooty's wand in excitement. Sooty tried to stop him – but it was too late! The magic took them back in time ...

2. Deep in the forest Sooty and the gang found two outlaws robbing the Sheriff. "Goodness!" cried Soo. "We must *do* something!"

3. But the Sheriff took Soo! "I'm Robin Hood," said one outlaw. "Little John and I were only taking back money stolen by the Sheriff."

4. The Sheriff thought Soo was beautiful. "Such big, dark eyes," he sighed. "Let's get married – tomorrow afternoon!"

5. "I don't *want* to marry the silly Sheriff," Soo told Maid Marian. "Anyway, he looks too much like my friend Matthew!"

6. Back in Robin's camp, an arrow brought the news of Soo's wedding. Sooty looked alarmed. Sweep and Scampi couldn't stop giggling!

7. It was the wedding day. Robin had a plan to rescue Soo. He had some strange *new* Merry Men with him!

8. Sooty took part in the archery contest. He beat Robin ... but only because he had a little help from naughty Scampi!

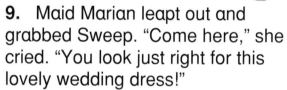

9. Maid Marian leapt out and grabbed Sweep. "Come here," she cried. "You look just right for this lovely wedding dress!"

10. It was time for the Sheriff to show his bride to the people. He took off the veil – and found that he was about to marry Sweep!

11. Robin swung from a rope and snatched the bride. Sooty and Scampi were ready and waiting with the getaway cart.

12. The outlaws raced off, but the Sheriff's men were very close behind. Soo looked for a fast way to help them!

13. Sooty and his friends were trapped by the Sheriff. They didn't know what to do. Then Sweep squeaked and pointed ...

14. Soo was driving the camper van! With bright headlights and a honking horn, it looked just like an angry dragon to the Sheriff.

15. Before they left the forest, Sooty gave Robin the horn from the van. "You can scare the Sheriff with dragon noises!" he laughed.

All Wrapped Up

Sooty, Sweep, Soo and Scampi are each tying up a Christmas present but have got their strings crossed. Which present belongs to whom? (*Answer on page 60.*)

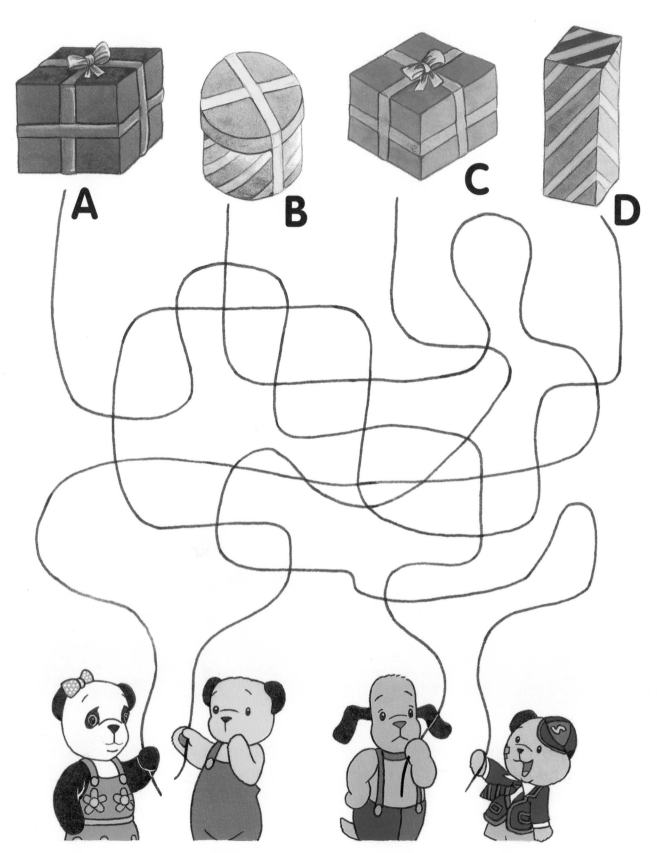

32

Sooty's Studio

As you can see, Sooty's clever at drawing – but he's not so good at colouring in. So he'd like you to finish off his picture, please, with your crayons or coloured pencils.

Sooty's Obstacle Race

Matthew has set up a bouncy castle in the park. But to reach it you have to take part in Sooty's Obstacle Race, with lots of surprises along the way. Just put your counters at the starting arrow, then throw a dice to start moving along the squares.

The first one to the bouncy castle is the winner. Whenever you land on a yellow square, you must squeak, "I want lots of bones for Christmas!" like Sweep; and when you land on a green square, you have to say, "Just wait until Matthew gets home!" in Soo's voice!

Cousin Paul lets you borrow his bike! Go forward 8 spaces.

Scampi's dropped his pocket money! Help him pick it all up and miss a turn.

You're out of breath! Miss a turn <u>or</u> go back 3 spaces.

Soo refreshes you with an ice-cold drink! Have an extra turn.

Mo stops you for a chat and won't stop talking! Go back 6 spaces.

Sweep blocks you path with a pile of bones he's dug up Miss a turn.

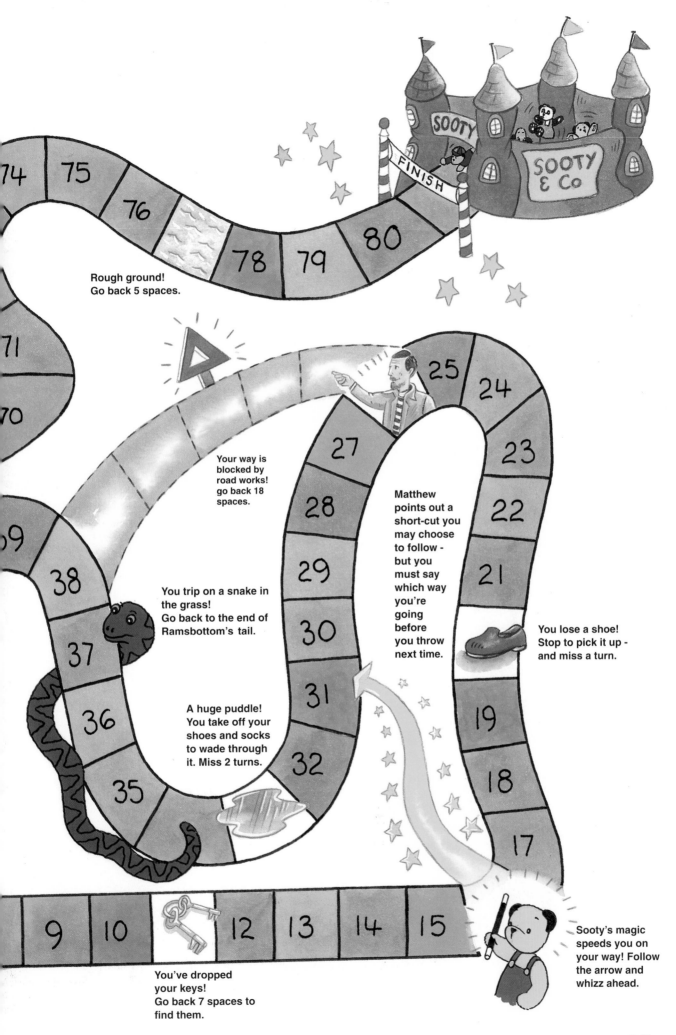

Rough ground!
Go back 5 spaces.

Your way is blocked by road works! go back 18 spaces.

You trip on a snake in the grass!
Go back to the end of Ramsbottom's tail.

Matthew points out a short-cut you may choose to follow - but you must say which way you're going before you throw next time.

You lose a shoe! Stop to pick it up - and miss a turn.

A huge puddle! You take off your shoes and socks to wade through it. Miss 2 turns.

You've dropped your keys! Go back 7 spaces to find them.

Sooty's magic speeds you on your way! Follow the arrow and whizz ahead.

FINISH

SOOTY

SOOTY & Co

35

Dear Matthew

Where is Sooty's favourite place for sand, sun and lots of fun? Blackpool, of course! He's been coming here for as long as he can remember. What a pity Matthew can't join his friends on this trip. Never mind – Sooty, Sweep, Soo and Scampi have sent him picture postcards ...

Dear Matthew,
I'm afraid I've eaten two sticks of rock today. One of them was a present for you... but it was a nice pink colour and just too tasty! Friday is like a holiday here for the donkeys - it's their day off!

Love Soo xx

What a day, Matthew!
This morning I buried a juicy bone on the beach. Then I went with Sooty, Soo and Scampi to the Pleasure Beach. Now it's tea time but I can't find my bone and I'm very hungry! See you soon.
Squeak, squeak,   Sweep

Dear Matthew,
Having a wonderful time. We've been up in the sky, almost as high as the clouds. Don't worry, we weren't flying a plane - we went in a lift to the top of Blackpool Tower. You can see for miles up there.
Don't work too hard,
    Sooty

Hi, Matthew,
I know what I'm going to be when I grow up - be a tram driver! These Blackpool trams are great. And during the illuminations they light some of them up with hundreds of bright bulbs. Blackpool beats school any day!
    Scampi

Party Time with Soo

It's so nice to get away from those boys for a while to show you two super ideas for a birthday party or special occasion ...

Camper Van Cake

Here's a cake that's really different, and it's not hard to make. Just ask a grown-up to cut a sponge cake into the two shapes shown. Cover the big piece in yellow icing, and the smaller one in white icing, then stick them together on a cake base. Pipe in the windows, the words on the sides, and the Sooty & Co. number plates – SSS 123. Finally, add four chocolate-covered biscuits for wheels, and Smarties for headlights!

Ramsbottom Puppet

Now for a simple, slithery puppet to keep your friends entertained! Find an old long sock – brown is best – and glue on two buttons for eyes, or make them from two little circles of white cloth or felt, as shown. Finish off these eyes with two blobs of a thick felt-tip pen. Put the sock over your hand and use your thumb and fingers to open and close Ramsbottom's mouth. You can also add a little forked tongue made out of a scrap of red card (perhaps from a cereal box).

Spot the difference

Here are two pictures of Sooty, Sweep, Soo and Scampi busy decorating their Christmas tree. They may look the same, but there are five differences in the bottom picture. Can you spot them? (*Answers on page 60.*)

TROUBLE UP AT THE MILL

1. One morning Matthew was in the shop waiting for the first customer to come in.

2. Suddenly Sooty popped up and asked for batteries for his computer game.

3. "You should play with *proper* toys like these," sighed Matthew. He showed Sooty two old-fashioned toys...

4...a whip-and-top...

5. ...and a little stick-and-hoop.

6. As Matthew talked about the days when he was a boy, a bandsman came past playing an old tune on a cornet.

7. "That's the trouble with living here," sighed Matthew. "Brass bands everywhere!"

8. He showed Sooty, Sweep, Soo and young Scampi more old-fashioned toys.

9. As he brought out a lovely doll in a frilly dress...

10. ...the bandsman came *into* the shop and played loudly. "Will you *please* get out!" yelled Matthew.

11. For breakfast Matthew dressed up in a flat cap and scarf. They were the clothes he would have worn a hundred years ago.

12. "We're having bacon, eggs, sausage, toast, jam and kippers!" Soo said, with a grin. "But for *you*, Matthew, just a bowl of thin soup!"

13. Matthew pulled a face. Old-fashioned food did not please him!

14. But later he decided to *show* Sooty, Sweep and Soo how good the old days were. Scampi stayed behind to look after the shop.

15. Soon the little yellow camper van pulled up outside an old mill near Manchester.

16. Matthew arrived on foot, of course – the *old* way of getting there!

17. Whilst Sooty, Sweep and Soo looked at the water wheel and people making cloth, Matthew found the office of the mill boss.

18. He sat in the big chair and fell asleep.

19. Moments later he turned into a grumpy Victorian boss from long ago! Now he had long whiskers!

20. Sweep came in and asked for his wages.

21. "You'll get wages when you do some work!" shouted Matthew. "Go and bring me a grumlin bar from the spraking shed."

22. Poor Sweep had no idea what that was, but he ran round the mill to find one.

23. Then he hurried back to the office.

24. Matthew was talking to Soo, and he turned angrily to Sweep.

25. "What do I want with a grumlin bar from the spraking shed? Fetch me a saggerknocker's bottom splint at once!"

26. Five minutes later, after another chase round the factory, Sweep arrived back, squeaking loudly at Matthew, who had fallen asleep.

27. "What!? You've got a saggerknocker's bottom? You poor thing!" cried Soo. "Oh, I see what you mean! Let's wake up the boss. Wake up, sir, wake up."

28. Matthew jumped and awoke, but it was the present-day again.

45

29. "Wakey, wakey, Matthew," Soo was saying.

30. "Oh? What? Where am I?" Matthew had been dreaming. "Oh, phew! I'm *not* a grumpy old boss after all!"

31. He was so pleased it had been a dream, he forgot all about the good old days.

32. Back at the shop he gave Sooty, Sweep, Soo and Scampi a £1 coin each.

33. But he was puzzled when he found something odd under the counter in the shop. What was it? *A saggerknocker's bottom splint!*

46

How's your Memory?

See how good you are at remembering what you've seen! Sooty has found all sorts of things in the shop and placed them on this tray. Look carefully at the picture for one minute, then cover it up and try to write down everything you've seen. Bet you can't remember *everything*!

Scampi's School Mystery

For one night only ... 'Inspector' Scampi and his teachers present the Missing Christmas Pudding Mystery! Can you work out how Scampi found the greedy teacher who couldn't resist the tasty pud?

1. Walking past the school, Scampi saw the kitchen window was wide open ...

2. Someone was taking the giant Christmas pudding. Scampi ran off to get help.

3. It was too late ... the pudding had gone. "It must be one of the five teachers," said the head teacher. "Ask them to do a written exam!" said Scampi brightly.

4. The five teachers sat down to do the test. As they wrote, Scampi watched carefully. Then he smiled and pointed to one of them. He had identified the greedy teacher!

Which teacher had taken the pud, and how did Scampi know? *(Answer on page 60.)*

Sooty goes to Hollywood

Sooty, Sweep, Soo and Scampi danced in a line as they finished a show in the theatre. Then they bowed and waved to the delighted audience, who clapped and clapped.

Back in the dressing room, the door burst open and in came a big man with a wide smile.

"Hi ... Max Silverdollar's the name. You were *great*, babes. I want you to make a film!" he cried.

"You'll be *stars* in Hollywood!"

"Hollywood?" inquired Soo. "Is that near Blackpool ...?"

"Heck, no. I mean Hollywood, California, babe – *in the United States of America*!" laughed Max.

The sun shone brightly as Sooty and his friends arrived at Max's studio in Hollywood.

"It's a bit bigger than your little camper van, eh?" said Max, pointing at a huge motor caravan which belonged to a famous film star.

"*Everything's* bigger over here! We make six films a day! But don't worry, babes – you've got a whole *week*. Here's your script. Any questions?"

"What sort of film is it?" asked Sooty.

"Oh, I don't know – but it'll be *big*. See you soon!" And with that, Max was gone.

It was a detective story. Sooty was the director as well as the star, and he and Sweep played detectives. Scampi was a master criminal, and Soo was a singer.

The time came for Soo's big scene. An actor raced up in a police car and screeched to a halt. But instead of jumping in, as she was supposed to do, Soo tapped angrily on the roof.

"You silly-billy!" she shouted.

"Fancy driving like that. You'll cause an accident!"

Sweep didn't like Hollywood – because you have to wear make-up! A lady kept coming to powder his nose to make him more handsome. In one scene Daisy Love, the famous actress, had to ask Sweep for help. But the cloud of powder round his head made him sneeze. Daisy jumped back in alarm and knocked over a big lamp. This knocked over another lamp, which then knocked over all the scenery!

"That's the last time I work with a *dog*!" shouted Daisy, running out.

ACHOOO

51

One morning Scampi and Sweep disappeared. Director Sooty looked everywhere for them.

"I saw them going into the hills," said a cameraman.

"Why would they do that?" asked Sooty. He soon found out, when he glanced over towards the hills with the famous sign that said HOLLYWOOD. It now read WOLLYHOOD.

"Bah!" cried Sooty. "They'll be in trouble when they come back!"

At last the film was finished, and it was time for the first performance of *Sooty Investigates*. Crowds of people waited outside the cinema as famous guests arrived.

When Sooty and the gang walked in, no one knew who they were. But a couple of hours later they were stars! They ran out of the cinema, with fans trying to kiss them!

"Fantastic, babes!" laughed Max. "I can't wait to see you in *Sooty II* and *Sooty III*. Why, they'll be – "

"I know ... *bigger still*," said Sooty. "But we aren't staying, Mr Silverdollar. We miss our home too much."

"What a shame," said Max. "Never mind, though. Your pal Matthew phoned ... and I sold him 500 videos of your film. He says they'll go like hot cakes in your little shop."

"I don't think so," sighed Soo, shaking her head. "Matthew couldn't sell ice lollies in the *desert* – but we still can't wait to see him again. Let's go, Sooty!"

53

Draw with Ramsbottom

How do, young 'uns! Bet you always wondered how a snake holds a pencil ... well, now you know! Anyway, here's an easy way to draw. Just get a big sheet of paper and, sketching lightly with a pencil, divide it into rough squares. Then copy my drawings square by square and you'll end up with a grand picture of Sooty and Sweep. With a bit of practice you'll soon be able to draw them without squares!

Which way, Paul?

Cousin Paul has about as much sense of direction as a fairground bumper car. Help him find his way back to the shop with his Christmas tree – before *next* Christmas comes round! (*Answer on page 60.*)

55

Clots on the Canal

I. Mo asked Sooty to take a brand new boat by canal to her friend in Yorkshire. Matthew stayed at home, as he gets seasick!

Sooty took command. Poor Sweep, Soo and Scampi had to do all the hard work ... and they were *not* very pleased.

2. That evening, Sooty's tired crew read one of Scampi's books. "Ha!" said Sweep. "If *we* were pirates we could take over *this* boat!"

3. "We're fed up scrubbing and cleaning," moaned Soo. "So we're playing pirates." "Sounds great! I think I'll *join* you!" said Sooty.

4. Sooty was now a pirate too. The rascals took turns at steering. They were all useless – but Scampi was really dangerous!

5. Sooty put too much washing-up liquid in the sink and the air was filled with bubbles. The pirates didn't notice they were now going in the wrong direction.

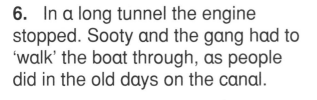

6. In a long tunnel the engine stopped. Sooty and the gang had to 'walk' the boat through, as people did in the old days on the canal.

7. Sweep had forgotten to put oil in the engine. So he had to pull the boat along, just as horses did before engines were invented.

57

8. "We'll wait till morning for this boat yard to open for repairs," said Sooty. Their boat pushed another one out of the way.

9. Next morning the boatman mistook Sooty's boat for the one they had pushed out of the way. And now he was painting it red!

10. Now with a smoky outboard motor, the pirates sailed on. "This is the way!" said Sweep, looking at his map upside-down!

11. A low bridge snapped off the chimney. The boat was a mess on the outside ... and then it flooded inside, as Scampi opened the lock.

12. Sweep was still muddled up. "Go right!" he squeaked, and Sooty turned the boat sharply. But no-one saw the big warning sign ...

13. The pirates were in a line of boats waiting to take away black mud. Splosh! "Stop!" they cried, but the crane driver didn't hear.

14. When they arrived on the River Thames in London, Sooty *knew* they were lost. "It's time for some quick magic!" he sighed.

15. In a flash the pirates appeared in Yorkshire. Mo and her friend were angry. What a pity there wasn't enough magic left to fix the boat!

Bye Bye, Everyone, Bye Bye!

That's all for now. Hope you enjoyed these stories about Sweep, Soo, Scampi and me. Oh, yes, and custard-pie face, too – Matthew, I mean!

We're all looking forward to meeting you again soon with new adventures to share. Here are the words to Sooty & Co., so you can sing along when you see us on TV.

Hey, ho, it's Sooty and Co., everybody say hello!
There's Sooty and Sweep. A panda called Soo,
And here comes Scampi too.
There'll be fun galore, with the terrible four,
Just you wait and see.
It's Sooty and Company, Sooty and Company!

Have a lovely year, love Sooty!

Answers

Sweep's Sausage Factory, page 21

S	W	E	E	P	L	N	P	S	E
C	A	N	U	Q	O	S	T	O	A
A	E	N	X	S	B	E	N	O	B
M	O	U	V	S	V	W	K	L	I
P	N	C	A	M	P	E	R	T	V
I	N	H	N	D	Q	P	A	B	H
V	W	S	C	N	S	O	O	T	Y
M	A	G	I	C	U	I	A	B	U
K	N	W	E	Z	N	S	I	Q	V
S	D	A	W	E	H	T	T	A	M

What's the Difference? page 22
1. The window is not coloured in
2. The licence plate is missing
3. The puddle is missing
4. The left front chair leg is missing
5. Sooty's left arm cannot be seen

All Wrapped Up, page 32
A. Sweep B. Soo C. Scampi
D. Sooty

Spot the difference, page 39
1. A balloon is missing
2. Sweep's ear is missing
3. Sweep has a pom-pom on his hat
4. A bauble is missing from the tree
5. Plaster on Scampi's face is missing

Scampi's School Mystery, page 48
Mr Wilson was guilty. To find the pudding thief Scampi simply looked for a left-handed person wearing a watch!

Which way, Paul? page 55

60

Join the Sooty Club
It's Magic

You'll get a personal letter from Sooty and his friends, a membership card, a badge with your name and a video of *Bubble Trouble*, a brilliant Sooty show now available only to Club Members. Not to mention two great face masks...two finger puppets...a Sooty story...a bookmark...a giant Sooty colouring book...a rainbow pencil disguised as Sooty's wand and an amazing Sooty conjuring trick. Magic!

We'll also send you the next issue of the Sooty magazine and birthday and Christmas cards. A year's membership is just £8.99 (plus 93p postage) with a 14 day no quibble money-back guarantee.

Return the coupon below (or a photocopy) to: Sooty Club, TV Town, PO Box 142, Horsham, RH13 5FJ. Credit card orders may call 01403 242727 or fax 01403 261555. Please ensure the coupon is filled in by an adult.

Please enrol the following as a member of The Sooty Club at £9.92 (inc postage).

Member's Full Name : _Stephen Moore_ Member's Address: _3 Ooka Moore Coste_

Post Code: _W1 9b1_ Date of birth: _13/11/90_

Your Name: _Stephen_ Address (if different): _____

_____ Post Code: _____

Name of child's parent or guardian (if not you): _____

❏ I enclose a cheque or postal order for £9.92 payable to Sooty Club

❏ Please charge the sum of £9.92 to my Access/Visa account.

Card number: | | | | | | | | | | | | | | | | | | Expiry Date: _____/_____

Data Protection Act: If you do **not** wish to receive other children's offers from us or companies we recommend, please tick this box ❏

WI